A IS FOR
APPLE PIE

AND OTHER LEARNING RHYMES

® Landoll, Inc.
Ashland, Ohio 44805
© 1991 Oyster Books Ltd.

ALPHABET PIE

A was an apple pie

B bit it

C cut it

D dealt it

E eat it

F fought for it

G got it

H had it

I inspected it

J jumped for it

K kept it

L longed for it

M mourned for it

N nodded at it

O opened it

P peeped in it

Q quartered it

R ran for it

S sang for it

T took it

U upset it

V viewed it

W wanted it

X,Y and Z all wished
for a piece in hand.

BELL HORSES

Bell horses, bell horses,
What time of day?
One o'clock, two o'clock,
Three and away.

Bell horses, bell horses,
What time of day?
Two o'clock, three o'clock,
Four and away.

Bell horses, bell horses,
What time of day?
Five o'clock, six o'clock,
Now time to stay.

THE COCK DOES CROW

The cock does crow
To let you know
If you be wise
'Tis time to rise;
For early to bed
And early to rise
Is the way to be healthy
And wealthy and wise.

Monday's Child

Monday's child is fair of face,

Tuesday's child is full of grace,

Wednesday's child is full of woe,

Thursday's child has far to go,

Friday's child is loving
and giving,

Saturday's child works hard
for his living,

And the child that is born on
the Sabbath day is pretty and
happy and good in every way.

ONE, TWO, THREE, FOUR

One, two, three, four
Mary at the cottage door,
Five, six, seven, eight,
Eating cherries off a plate.

A DOZEN IS TWELVE

A dozen is twelve,
Or four times three.
Half a dozen is six,
As plain as can be.

FIVE LITTLE MONKEYS

Five little monkeys walked along the shore

One went sailing, then there were four.

Four little monkeys climbed up a tree

One tumbled down, then there were three.

Three little monkeys found a pot of glue

One got stuck in it, then there were two.

Two little monkeys found a currant bun

One ran away with it, then there was one.

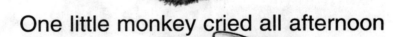

One little monkey cried all afternoon

So they put him in an airplane
And sent him to the moon!

BOW-WOW, SAYS THE DOG

Bow-wow, says the dog,
Mew, mew, says the cat,
Grunt, grunt goes the hog,
And squeak goes the rat.
Tu-whu, says the owl,
Caw, caw, says the crow,
Quack, quack, says the duck,
And what cuckoos say you know.

LITTLE SHIPS

Little ships must keep close to shore;
Larger ships may venture more.

MANNERS

Manners in the dining room,
Manners in the hall,
If you don't behave yourself
You shan't have none at all.

As I Was Going To St Ives

As I was going to St Ives,
I met a man with seven wives.
Each wife had seven sacks,
Each sack had seven cats,
Each cat had seven kits,
Kits, cats, sacks and wives,
How many were going to St Ives?

THIRTY DAYS HAS SEPTEMBER

Thirty days has September,
April, June, and November;
All the rest have thirty-one;
Excepting February alone;
And that has twenty-eight days clear
And twenty-nine in each leap year.

MR EAST GAVE A FEAST

Mr East gave a feast
Mr North laid the cloth;
Mr West did his best;
Mr South burnt his mouth
Eating a cold potato.

SPRING IS SHOWERY

Spring is showery, flowery, bowery
Summer is hoppy, croppy, poppy
Autumn is wheezy, sneezy, freezy
Winter is slippy, drippy, nippy.

RAINY RHYMES

When the peacock loudly calls,
Then look out for rain and squalls.

Rain before seven,
Fine before eleven.

If chickens roll in the sand,
Rain is sure to be at hand.

When the clouds appear like rocks and towers,
The earth's refreshed by frequent showers.

A sunshiny shower
Won't last half an hour.

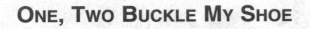

One, two,
   buckle my shoe.

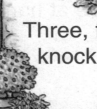

Three, four,
   knock at the door.

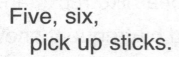

Five, six,
   pick up sticks.

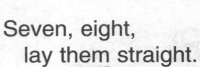

Seven, eight,
   lay them straight.

Nine, ten,
   a big fat hen.